Under the City

Under the City
by David Lavine
photographs
by Ira Mandelbaum

Doubleday & Company, Inc., Garden City, New York

All photographs are by Ira Mandelbaum
with the exception of those credited otherwise.

Library of Congress Catalog Card Number 67–10680
Copyright © 1967 by David Lavine
All Rights Reserved
Printed in the United States of America
9 8 7 6 5 4 3 2

To Nancy

Contents

Under the City

Chapter One
Digging Under the City

Stretching beneath the flesh of a city are the arteries and veins that give it its life. Sometimes, the humming telephone wires, the insulated electric cables, and the other vitals of a great metropolis lie only a few inches beneath the blue pavement. If your toes could feel the hidden power beneath the ground, they would tingle with a surging energy.

Below this uppermost network of wires is more of the city's underground life. Water mains, set four feet deep in northern cities so they won't freeze during winter, are all but forgotten until

one breaks and thousands of gallons go spouting up through the pavement. Next to the mains are the gas pipes, which must be well away from the high-voltage wires to lessen any chance of explosion in case of a leak. Further down, about ten or twelve feet from the surface, are sewer lines carrying waste and drain water to treatment plants for disposal. Then, sometimes hundreds of feet below the city streets are vast concrete tunnels, roaring with water which has traveled from far-off reservoirs and watersheds.

This is the pattern, but each city makes it own particular cnanges because of muddy soil hidden streams, or simply an earlier utility which is using the underground space. Much of this book will concentrate on New York because of its size and its variety of tubes, tunnels, and deep sub-basements. Yet, many other cities can claim proud "firsts" in underground construction—like Boston, which had the nation's first electrified subway, and San Francisco, which built the first underground municipal garage. New Orleans has led the way with a vehicular tunnel that runs itself, automatically collecting tolls, regulating traffic signals, and purifying the air. In Chicago, Greyhound Bus Lines uses a terminal that is entirely below the street.

Still, New York remains the most crowded city, both below and above the ground. The men who repair the utilities say that there are places under the street where you couldn't fit in so much as a lead pencil. Yet, all these wires and veins must not interfere with 700 miles of subway track and two vast underground railway stations. At Thirty-second Street, next to Pennsylvania Station, there are *five* separate levels of transportation tunnels. The three city subway lines, the Hudson Tubes, and

LEFT: Standing at the bottom of a utility shaft 150 feet beneath the ground, one has an unusual view of the maze of electric and steam cables.

NEXT PAGE: Cars are whisked into a parking garage hundreds of feet beneath the street.

13

the Pennsylvania Railroad, all have their own stations built one
on top of the other.

Nor is that all, for under the city streets there are movie
theaters, pet shops, stores where sporting equipment, luggage,
and even rare books are sold. You can buy an African spear in
a curio shop near a subway station. Or you can plan a trip to

Everything from rare books to talking birds is sold in the underground concourse of Rockefeller Center.

Africa in a travel agency in the sub-surface arcade of Rockefeller Center. From candy bars to seven-course meals, it's all available beneath the sidewalk. Come along and visit the under-the-city world. It's an exciting experience and one you won't forget.

17

In a basement in Rockefeller Center you can even find a conveyor belt for tacos or the beginnings of Christmas decorations for Rockefeller Plaza.

The first thing that the explorer needs is a good map. The maze of pipes, cables, and mains beneath New York streets is more tangled than the densest part of the Amazon jungles. But if you want to put down a power line, you cannot chop your

way through the streets as you might hack out a jungle trail.
One wrong move with an air drill can knock out telephone
lines, cause a gas leak or send blue sparks of electricity flying
into the air.

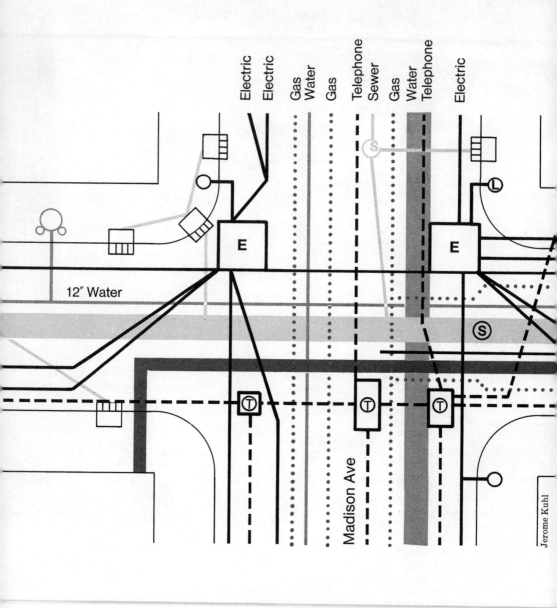

An artist's view of the utility lines under an uncrowded corner in New York City. On maps of busier crossroads, it's almost impossible to sort out the tangle of pipes and mains. (Courtesy of Con Edison)

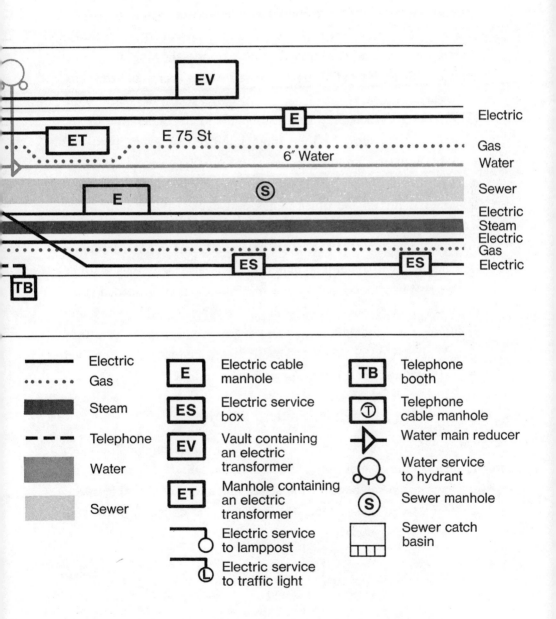

E 75 St

EV

E — Electric

ET

6″ Water — Gas
Water

S — Sewer

E — Electric
Steam
Electric
Gas

ES   ES — Electric

TB

	Electric		E	Electric cable manhole		TB	Telephone booth
	Gas		ES	Electric service box		T	Telephone cable manhole
	Steam		EV	Vault containing an electric transformer			Water main reducer
	Telephone		ET	Manhole containing an electric transformer			Water service to hydrant
	Water			Electric service to lamppost		S	Sewer manhole
	Sewer		L	Electric service to traffic light			Sewer catch basin

Many years ago, the federal government drew a street-by-street map of all the utilities below the ground in Manhattan, but New York changes so rapidly that this map is now out-of-date. When the city puts in a new sewer line, everything else is moved out of its way. If a new power station is built, underground cable for miles around must be shifted.

The Telephone Company, the Water Department, the Public Works and Transit Authority all have maps showing their own services. Consolidated Edison, which takes care of the gas, electricity, and steam in New York City, keeps the most complete records. When they have a big job to do under one of the busy city street corners, they must know about every pipe and wire beneath the ground. It would be an expensive mistake to start a tunnel for a gas main and then find that there is no space left between the other mains and cables to get it through. The mapmakers of Consolidated Edison go over their own records and then those of the city departments and other companies that might have something under the corner where they will be working. When they have all the information that is needed, they draw an underground map that shows the location, size, and depth of every manhole, line, and main in the street. Yet, they cannot always be positive of what is below the surface, and then there is nothing to do but dig and take a look.

Open-Ditch Tunneling

Whenever new electric cables, gas mains, or telephone lines are needed, a tunnel must be carved in the earth. If the utilities do not have to go far beneath the street and there is available space in the crowded sub-surface, the pavement is chopped away and

An open-ditch trench is cut to make way for a new subway tunnel.

But first the pipes, mains, and conduits must be moved out of the way.

Once the trench is cleared of utility lines, supporting beams are installed and the trench is deepened.

25

an open trench is dug. While motorists honk their horns at the barricades and passers-by stop to stare, construction workers lay down steel or concrete shells into the trenches.

All of the city's early subways were dug using open-ditch tunneling. But as more people rode the subways, tunnels had to be built beneath each other. One tunnel recently finished in New York has five other transit lines overhead. In places, there are only a couple of feet of rock and iron between the bottom two tunnels. During construction, the workers had to be sure that there were no trains passing above them before they exploded their dynamite.

Open-ditch tunneling is still used when new subway routes are being placed. However, great care must be taken with the utilities that are already beneath the street. These cables, pipes, and conduits must be moved to another part of the street without interrupting any of the services.

Deep Digging

Deep tunneling hundreds of feet below the surface is an even more difficult job. The men who do this work are called sand hogs, and they are equally handy with dynamite, pickaxes, and air drills. Sand hogs also do a bit of railroading, for tracks must often be laid on a tunnel floor to move in heavy equipment and move out muck—the sand hogs' word for loose dirt, stones, and mud. To get to their tunnel site, sand hogs start by digging down, sinking a large shaft into the ground as far as they must

LEFT: A bulldozer and crane clear away dirt and rocks from the open ditch.

NEXT PAGE: Sand hogs set dynamite at the far end of this new subway tunnel 250 feet beneath the surface.

go. The shaft usually is wide enough so an elevator can fit inside, carrying the men and equipment back and forth to the tunnel.

Once underground, sand hogs prefer to work in solid rock, for there is less chance of a slide or a cave-in. Holes are drilled into the rock in the face, or far end, of the tunnel, and small charges of dynamite are then laid in the holes. The sand hogs retreat a safe distance and the explosives are set off. When the pieces of rock have stopped flying and the smoke and dust have been drawn off by ventilators, the men scoop the rubble into tiny railroad cars. The cars take it to the elevator shaft, from where it is lifted to the surface.

Much of the rock beneath the city is not solid and has cracks, or "faults," running through it. When the sand hogs work in this sort of rock they take a risk every time they have to set off a dynamite charge. Even though beams are put up to support the roof of the tunnel after each blast, there is always a danger that something will give way before the heavy timbers are firmly in place. Later, as the job goes on, iron rods bolt sections of the roof together permanently.

Frequently when digging under the city, sand hogs meet quicksand, deep pockets of mud, and hidden streams. A map put out by one construction company shows Manhattan Island as it was in 1609, when the Dutch were still calling it Nieuw Amsterdam. The island was dotted with streams and ponds which have since been buried under mounds of earth and concrete. But some of these underground streams refused to disappear entirely. In lower Manhattan, Minetta Stream, which the Indians once paddled, now leaks into basements whenever there is a heavy rain. And other hidden brooks are almost as mischievous.

The map also shows that many of the concrete and asphalt streets have been stolen from the Hudson and the East rivers.

This is called "filled" land, for the river bed has been filled in with rocks and dirt to support construction. Almost all the piers where giant ocean liners now tie up were once river water. But the Hudson has not forgotten, and when storms come roaring across the lower bay, the river rises and reclaims the bordering West Side avenues.

Most builders try to avoid sinking deep foundations into such soft parts of the island, for it can cost a vast amount of money to pump out the mushy soil and harden the quicksand. Yet the new World Trade Center, which will be the world's largest building, will be erected on spongy, filled land. The Trade Center will be like an enormous concrete bubble with its foundations keeping it firmly balanced in the mud. If this sounds impossible, you should know that there is a tunnel from Manhattan to Brooklyn which also rests on a good deal of mud, and it hasn't floated away with any cars inside . . . yet!

Before any tunnel is started, tests in the ground below are made by drilling down with a hollow pipe along the tunnel's route. If the test borings show mud or quicksand, then the digging must be done under pressure so that the earth and rock are held back, preventing cave-ins. By continuously pumping compressed air into the tunnel, it is kept safe. It is something like blowing up a leaky balloon underwater. If you blow steadily, the balloon will remain inflated, and the water will not be able to get inside through the holes.

The sand hogs enter a tunnel which is under pressure by first passing through an air lock. The lock is a steel chamber in the mouth of the tunnel, with a door on each side, one of which is always sealed. Once the sand hogs are inside the lock, the entrance door is sealed and the air pressure is slowly built up.

NEXT PAGE: After the rock is blasted away, the tunnel's supporting beams are installed.

31

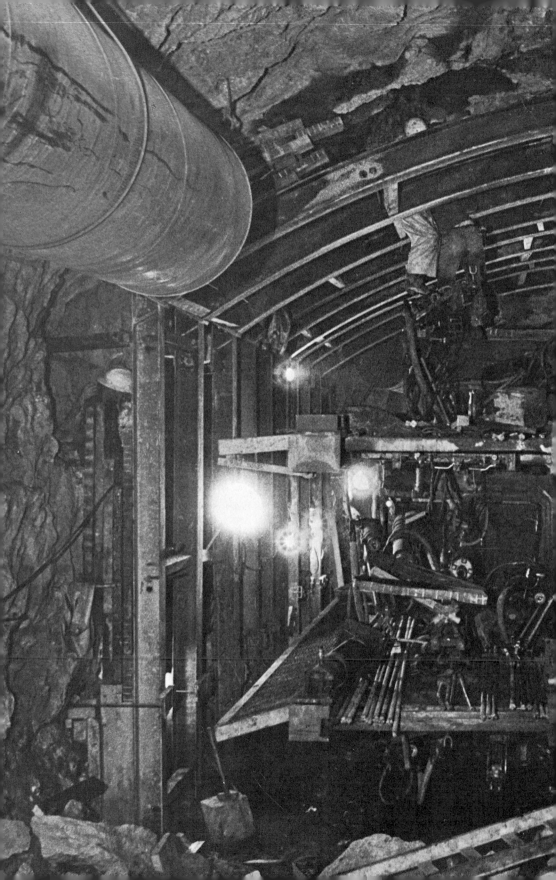

Since the pressure in the tunnel is much greater than that out-side, the sand hogs, like deep-sea divers, must give their bodies time to adjust to the change. Finally, when the air pressure is high enough in the chamber, the tunnel door is opened and the men can start work. This procedure is reversed when the men leave the job. They go into the lock through the tunnel door,

which is then sealed behind them. The air pressure is then gradually lowered until the outer door can be opened safely.

Today, working under pressure, while still risky, is routine to sand hogs. However, many early tunneling jobs ended in tragedy. The first attempt to force a tunnel under the Hudson, using compressed air to hold back the river, resulted in the deaths of

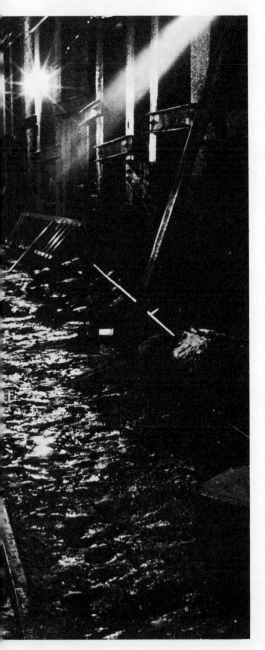

Here, temporary tracks have been laid in the tunnel to haul out dirt and rocks.

NEXT PAGE: Sand hogs must go into this compression chamber before and after working in a tunnel under pressure. (Photo by Richard Saunders, Scope Associates)

twenty men. Too much pressure was forced into the tunnel and a hole was blown in the roof. The water rushed in, drowning every sand hog.

When sand hogs burrow deeply enough in the earth, they often discover some buried trace of history. In Chicago, the crew that dug the underground municipal garage found charred objects from the Great Fire of 1871, as well as buried seashells showing that Lake Michigan had once extended over much of the Windy City. No big construction job can be done in New York without turning up some arrowheads or flintlocks or the cannon balls from the Revolutionary War. Below the Manhattan shoreline, a Dutch ship from Nieuw Amsterdam days was found with the captain's clay pipe still unbroken in his cabin.

But it takes more than old bones to stop a sand hog, for he knows he is doing the important job of keeping the life of the city moving beneath its pavements and streets.

Chapter Two
Utilities

Many New Yorkers believe that there are alligators living under the city. It is said that unwanted baby alligators, brought up from Florida as souvenirs, have been dropped in the drains, and have grown to enormous size. Sadly, like the tale of the blind fish in the water pipes and the wild cats roaming the subway tunnels, this is nothing more than a good story. It is far too cold in the drains for alligators to survive more than a few days.

But there is a nasty and dangerous animal that lurks beneath the surface of the city. Anyone who opens a manhole to work

on an electric cable, gas pipe, or sewer line keeps a sharp lookout for the gleaming red eyes of the city rat. These creatures grow larger than a weasel and are much meaner. Their sharp teeth can bite right through a leather boot and carry disease and infection.

Rats seem to thrive in the murky hollows of the city. An old-timer who worked on a subway tunnel under the East River swore that rats lived there under pressure without ever having gone through the compression chamber. No one could explain how they got in, but these rodents became so bold that lunches weren't safe unless they were hung on wires.

Another ugly pest is the giant water beetle, which looks something like an over-sized cockroach. These beetles feast on grease and dirt and live by the hundreds at the bottom of some man-holes. Occasionally, when they are disturbed, they fly into the sky, causing women to shriek in fright.

There are about a third of a million manholes in New York City, ranging in size from a space only big enough for a single man to vaults the size of a large room. Almost all the utilities—gas, electricity, telephone, water, and sewers—have manholes leading down beneath the street. In them are the valves, levers, switches, and controls for the pipes and cables, which the maintenance men must check on and repair regularly.

Fortunately, not all have unpleasant creatures scurrying about. But most of them are hot, dirty, and smelly. In winter, they aren't too bad, but the summer sun can turn the narrow holes into ovens. Air blowers must often cool the underground space before the men can do their work. As often as possible, water

LEFT: Workmen hose out a manhole with water before entering to make repairs.

NEXT PAGE: Inside a manhole, a workman checks for defects in telephone cables.

41

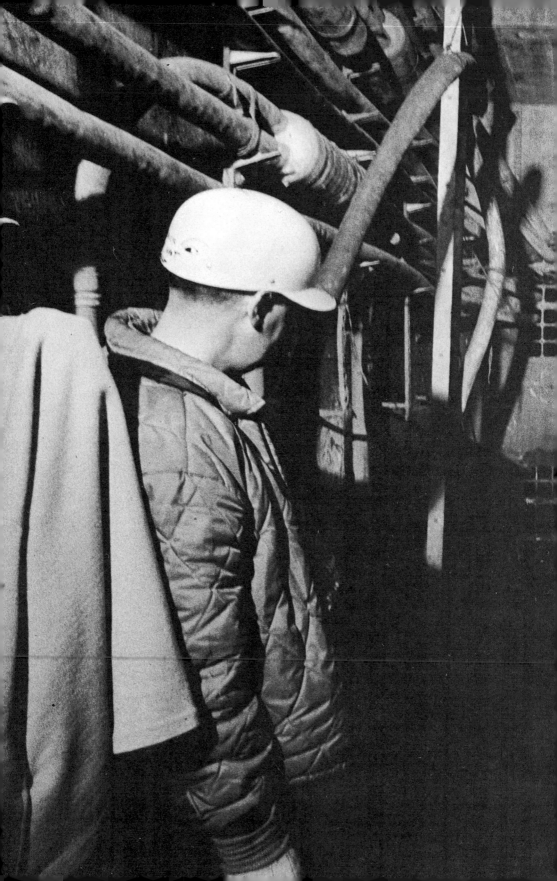

trucks hose out the manholes, but the dirt and grime of a big city quickly slips back inside.

Every utility using the space beneath the street has the same worry. Will there be a failure in service today? The lines are so close to each other that a break in one may mean trouble for all. Usually the most serious are water-main breaks, for the erupting water can snap sewer pipes, short-circuit electric cables, and wash away the telephone conduits. Therefore, whenever news of a water-main break is flashed, all emergency repair crews swing into action.

Gas explosions can also shatter pipes nearby. Gas from a leaky main may gather unnoticed in a manhole until a discarded cigarette triggers a blast. To prevent this, gas companies keep a constant check on their mains and follow up all complaints of suspicious odors.

The most famous utility inspector was Smelly Kelly, whose nickname was earned by his super-sensitive nose. Sewer breaks, gas leaks—Kelly found them all. One whiff and he could follow the scent back to the break in the pipe. Modern inspectors, however, are accompanied by detecting machines which are almost, but perhaps not quite, as good as Smelly Kelly.

Electricity

Charging beneath the city streets are thousands of volts of electric power. Traffic signals, elevators, subway trains, toasters, and television sets are a few of the useful items that depend on electricity for their existence. Without electric power, the services of any large city would come to a stop.

The usual amount of power needed to run most household

Looking upward toward street level from the bottom of a manhole.

appliances is 120 volts. Look on the outside of any light bulb and you will find that they are all stamped for this voltage. But this does not mean that there is a single underground cable carrying 120 volts from the power station to your house or apartment.

In New York, most of the city's power is made at large generating stations by huge turbines. This power is brought to various sub-stations throughout the city. At times, as many as three hundred and forty-five thousand volts travel along a single cable, which Consolidated Edison calls its "backbone cable." At the sub-station, this vast power is stepped down, which means that the voltage is reduced and sent out again on smaller lines. There are so many underground cables running to and from the sub-stations that the tangle of wires looks like a giant's plate of macaroni. The power in these smaller lines is still too strong for our homes. It must be reduced once more by passing through a transformer, which is usually buried beneath the pavement. The transformers reduce the power to the voltage that we use in our homes, and an underground wire brings it into our basements. Here it passes through a meter that will record the amount of current we draw every time we flick on a light or turn on the television set.

While the city usually produces enough power for its users, there are peak periods when it buys power from other utility companies. Similarly, the city sells excess power to other parts of the northeast when it is not needed. This is done through a

LEFT: The surge of electric power starts in these huge turbines at one of the city's many central generating stations.

NEXT PAGE: These buttons, levers, and dials control the amount of electricity that is sent from the central generators into underground cables.

power network, which can automatically call for current in areas hundreds of miles away.

While the power grid is a way for utilities to extend each other a helping hand, it can also lead to disastrous results if there are sudden and violent demands for power. Not too long ago, a power failure in the northern section of the grid sent an automatic demand for voltage to the next generating station. The demand was so sudden and so overwhelming that the second generating station failed and, in turn, relayed an automatic call for power to the next utility station. In a matter of seconds, this series of unusual power drains triggered one failure after another. As each city's power generators shut themselves down rather than burn up, they put out an automatic call to generators in the neighboring city, causing them to overload and shut down. The result was that in a matter of seconds the entire northeastern part of the United States was blacked out.

The trouble in power lines is usually minor, though. Nevertheless, repairmen take careful precautions when they go into a manhole. They stand on rubber mats, wear heavy rubberized gloves, and use insulated tools. For any high-voltage repair, the power is also switched off. A tracer current, which is a very low voltage amount of power, is sent along the cable, and the meter shows where the trouble is. Usually, it's a matter of replacing a piece of equipment or tightening a joint which has become loosened in the manhole. But if there is a break in the cable, the entire section must be drawn out and replaced.

Most of the big cities in our nation use AC or alternating

ABOVE: Working in a vault under the sidewalk, these repairmen use protective, rubberized gloves and insulated equipment to fix a step-down transformer. (Photo by Myron Ehrenberg. Courtesy of Con Edison)

BELOW: In a manhole beneath the street a workman splices electric cabling. (Photo by Myron Ehrenberg. Courtesy of Con Edison)

current. Parts of New York, however, still use an additional web of DC, or direct current, cables. This older and more expensive way of making electricity goes back to the days when inventor Thomas Edison first produced electric power. His gas company, Edison Illumination, put down underground lines when automobiles were still rare and nearly everyone traveled by horse and carriage. Hansom-cab drivers worried about old Dobbin's iron shoes striking exposed wires, but Mr. Edison buried the cable too carefully for that.

Even a man of Edison's imagination would be surprised at how a high-voltage cable is protected today. Oil inside a lead pipe surrounds the insulated copper wires. Because the wires get sizzling hot and expand as power surges through them, the oil is kept under pressure. At night, when less power is needed, the copper wires cool down. Without the oil pressure, the insulation around the wires would become loose, something like a bandage around a twisted ankle after the swelling has gone away. In electric lines this can quickly lead to dangerous short circuits and fires.

Steam

Electric power is not alone in making the ground beneath the streets hot. Live steam sweeps through steel pipes, which wear asbestos jackets and overcoats of concrete. Most of the steam comes from the power plants that produce electric current. In New York, much of lower Manhattan has steam mains beneath the pavement. Many buildings find it cheaper to buy steam to heat their offices than to have a furnace in the basement. Steam is now also used to turn the generators that provide air condition-

A steam valve is attached to heat a New York Central railway car.

ing for many skyscrapers. Restaurants keep food warm with steam, cleaners use it to press a pair of pants, and the New York Central Railroad brings in steam to heat its railroad cars on chilly days.

Men who take care of other utilities blame steam mains for many of their troubles. They claim some of the fierce heat is always escaping and causing breaks in their utility lines. Sometimes, on cold mornings when ghostly mists dance up from manholes, it looks as if all the pipes are leaking steam into the air. But we are not looking at steam, for it is an invisible gas. What we see is a water vapor produced when the cold air hits the hot steam pipes and condenses. Enough of this vapor going skyward may signal a break somewhere.

Repairmen can also check at the plants to see if the pressure gauge has dropped. If the pressure is off, it usually means that always escaping and causing breaks in their utility lines. Sometimes, though, the break is in the main itself, and it will be necessary to cut into the pavement and slip another pipe over the leaking part of the main. This is a tricky job and has to be done with great care so that the new sleeve is tightly sealed onto the old pipe, and no further leakage will occur.

Gas

While New York steam is made by large generators in the city, the gas used for cooking or heating comes from natural gas fields in the southern and southwestern parts of the United States. The

LEFT: A ghostly trail of water vapor rises from a manhole on a chilly morning.

NEXT PAGE: In a specially built utilities tunnel under the East River, a huge main (on the right) brings natural gas between two of New York's boroughs. (Photo by Myron Ehrenberg. Courtesy of Con Edison)

gas travels across the nation in underground pipes at very high pressures. When it reaches the city, it has a thrust of 800 pounds per square inch, far too powerful for immediate use, as it would blow a kitchen stove apart if it went directly into our homes. Like the current in high-voltage cable, the gas pressure must be reduced.

The first step in the reduction is usually taken outside the city. Here the gas is channeled into larger pipes which allow it to expand and thereby lessen its thrust. Once the gas is inside the city mains, the pressure must be lowered again before it reaches our homes. This is done in long chambers underneath the street, which have more reducing valves and pipes.

Before the fields of natural gas were discovered, this fuel had to be made locally. At the time of our Civil War, anyone with a factory and a large furnace could manufacture gas by shooting oil over red-hot coke. Gas companies sprang up overnight, and each one insisted on laying its own mains. Because of the waste and expense, most of these companies went out of business, leaving only their unseen mains as a token that they had once been part of the city. Under Manhattan's Third Avenue, over a dozen of these unused mains lie side by side. To rip them out would mean uprooting the entire avenue and would cost far too much.

Water

The oldest pipes in the city were found near the Bowery. These were water pipes of hollow logs put down by Aaron Burr after the Revolutionary War. They were supposed to go up to the northern end of Manhattan to take water from the Bronx River, but instead Burr pumped water from a deep well. He was really more interested in banking than in supplying the island with water, but his old enemy, Alexander Hamilton, then Secretary of the Treasury, kept him from opening a bank. Burr outwitted Hamilton with the charter for his water company, which said he could use the profits for any purpose. With the money he made from the water lines, Burr started the Manhattan Bank, which is today the Chase Manhattan Bank and one of the nation's

Workmen inspect water pipe dating from Revolutionary days, found in lower Manhattan. (Photo by the Chase Manhattan Bank)

59

largest. Hamilton never forgave Mr. Burr, and the city's first water lines led to the famous duel in which Burr shot and killed Hamilton.

Getting enough water is a problem for our thirsty cities. Most large communities build reservoirs on high ground to capture the rainfall and the overflow of streams swollen during the spring thaw. From here, the water is purified and then pours down into underground mains. Other cities make use of nearby lakes and rivers. Cleveland, for example, has a tunnel like a huge straw which sucks water from Lake Erie.

The eight million people of New York City drink water

trapped hundreds of miles away and sent in three vast tunnels that finally dip eight hundred feet under the street. These long-distance water lines are the deepest of New York's many tunnels and conduits, and pumping stations throughout the city send the water into a network of high- and low-pressure mains.

The low-pressure mains, usually about four feet below the street surface, bring New Yorkers their water for washing and drinking. In skyscrapers and tall apartment buildings, the water pressure must be increased by individual pumps in the basement so it will reach the top floors. The second set of pipes carry water from pumping stations at very high pressure and are linked

Here, water from a broken main has washed away the supporting soil and rock, giving an unexpected view beneath the street.

NEXT PAGE: Water from underground pipes shoots hundreds of feet into the air as firemen battle a blaze. (Photo by The New York Times)

to special hydrants in crowded downtown sections. These are for fire fighting, and when the hoses are connected, it takes several men to hold them as the water shoots high into the air.

The New York Water Supply System, which funnels over a billion gallons of water into the underground mains, was considered limitless. But years of drought have dried out many of the reservoirs, and the city may soon start desalting ocean water. If it does, the next great tunnel will lead into the Atlantic.

Sewers

Sewer lines are usually placed beneath the other utilities (except the deepest water tunnels) at a depth of from ten to twelve feet. This allows good drainage for the pipes that carry waste from city buildings to the small sewer pipes running down both sides of the street. These, in turn, connect with the larger intercepter sewers, which are big enough to drive a truck through. The intercepter sewer carries the waste to a sewage-disposal plant. There are also separate sewer lines for rain water. The water drains into catch basins located at street corners, which are connected to the underground sewer lines.

Sewer lines are usually made of concrete or hardened iron, but in Boston, much of the main tunnel is wood. Most cities have rock a few feet below the surface, but Boston is built on a marsh. Unlike the more solid tunnels, the wooden sewers are somewhat flexible and can float suspended in the mud without having to be anchored in stone.

Telephones

Dial a call to a friend on a city phone and a thousand relay switches are sent into action. If you could watch your voice, you would see it routed from the wire of your receiver to a thick underground cable. Here, there are hundreds of pairs of wires, one for talking and one for listening. Like a spark in a maze, the automatic dialing system seeks out a pair of wires that are not in use and, through relay switches, speeds your voice from

In an open-ditch trench workmen install new concrete conduits that will hold underground telephone cables.

cable to cable as it travels to your friend's house. There is never one set path, and you might call your friend every night about homework and have your connection made through different underground wires each time.

If you opened an underground cable, the insides would look like a cord of multicolored threads. The pair you are using might be blue, orange, red, or yellow. The different colors help the phone man when he has to make repairs. Most cable is kept under air pressure to prevent water from seeping in. If there is a tiny leak, an alarm rings in the central office, indicating where the break is that must be fixed.

Sometimes, the trouble is in a pair of wires. In the sub-basement vault of the central office, where thousands of wires pass upward to the automated switchboard, a "beep beep beep" signaler is hooked into the bad pair. Then, using a meter, the repairman measures the approximate spot where the sound stops. Next he goes to the manhole in the street nearest the trouble spot. Usually the bad cable can be pulled through into the manhole. Before opening the cable, the repairman plugs it at both ends so the air cannot escape. Then he searches through the different colored wires with a listening device that looks like a thin metal pencil. When he hears the beeps signaling, he knows that he has found the bad wires.

Sometimes the entire cable must be replaced, and a new one is "snaked" from one manhole to the next, several hundred feet away. A stiff metal snaking wire is pushed through the conduit and hooked up to a pulley on a truck. The telephone cable is then attached to the wire and pulled through.

The phone company is usually planning many years ahead when it puts down the concrete conduits which hold the under-

Some of the telephone cables must be placed in steel pipes instead of concrete, particularly if they pass near steam mains.

ABOVE: The cables under the street pass into the sub-basement vault of a central telephone company office.

RIGHT: The many pairs of wires inside the cable are connected to this frame board in the central office, where thousands of calls are routed to homes and office buildings.

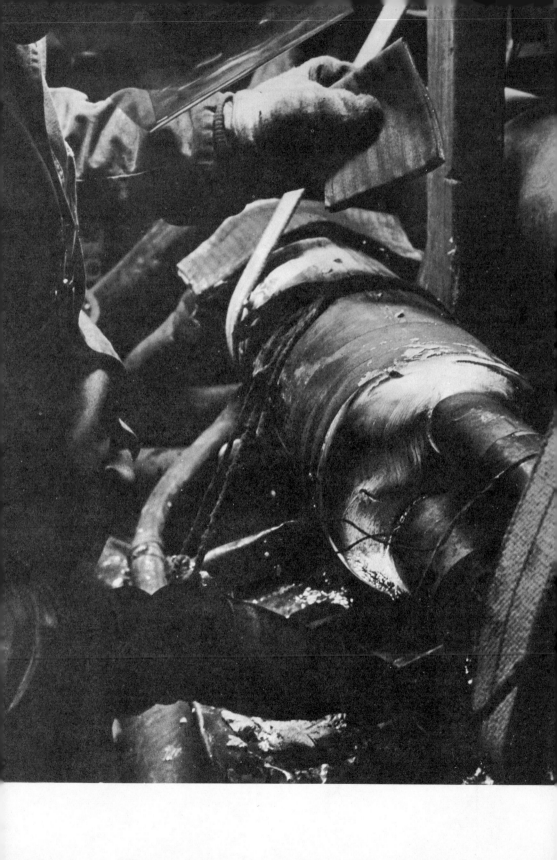

ground cable. Extra sections of the hollow conduits are laid. Then when more lines are needed, new cable can be pulled through this unused space without digging again. There must be space for future lines, as the demand for phones is always increasing.

Companies piping music into restaurants, private detective agencies with burglar alarm systems, and even the Police and Fire Departments often rent space in the conduits for their own lines. In New York, the Telephone Company also takes care of the lines leading to stop lights, and the new electronic system for

LEFT: Making repairs in a manhole, a workman covers faulty telephone cables with a lead jacket to keep them airtight and watertight.

BELOW: The repairman must find the faulty pair of wires inside the cable!

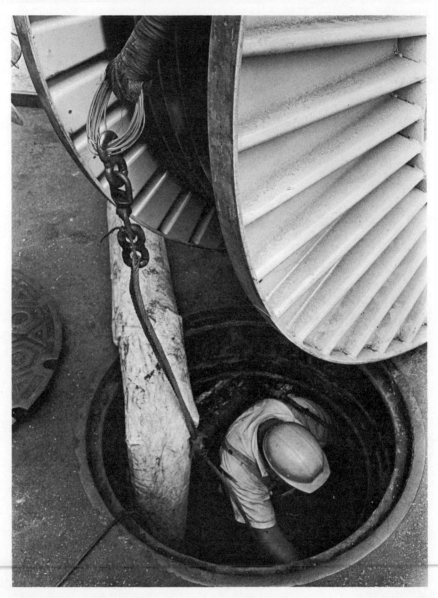

ABOVE: A telephone cable must be replaced, and the new one is unrolled from a huge spool and drawn down into a manhole.

RIGHT: At the end of the block a pulley hauls the new cable through to the next manhole.

72

automatic switching of signals according to the traffic flow will also be routed through the conduits.

Television programs also use the telephone lines to travel from the studio to the broadcasting stations. These lines are called coaxial cables and are composed of woven strands of copper which carry the sound and picture signals together. In New York, the cables pass through a special room in a telephone central office and then lead to a sub-basement in the Empire State Building, where the programs are transmitted from the antennae of the world's highest aerial.

Pneumatic Tubes

Western Union, which uses telephone conduits in New York and other cities, still has some steel tubes beneath the streets of Manhattan. Inside, there is enough space for a metal cylinder holding a telegram to speed with a whoosh of compressed air as it is blown from one office to another.

Until a few years ago, the Post Office had a similar system of tubes between a number of its stations. Mail was sent along in a metal "torpedo" about the width of a human being. In fact, there is an old picture showing an underground "astronaut" strapped into one of these metal torpedoes as he was about to be launched on a successful sub-surface journey. As the number of letters increased each year, it became simpler—though not as fast—to send the mail by truck.

Now the only other pneumatic-tube system in New York is one that goes from the Federal Treasury Building to another government building at Bowling Green. The government refuses to discuss this line, because it is often used to ship contraband, like narcotics, seized in raids.

74

Old Pipes and Tunnels

With the crowd of utilities beneath the surface, every inch of space is precious. Sometimes a disused main will serve a new purpose. Consolidated Edison took one of its six-foot-wide gas pipes which was no longer in service, and laid new high-pressure gas pipe inside of it. In Chicago, the Water Department salvaged an abandoned railway tunnel which had once run along a sixty-two-mile underground route. In the past, the tiny trains had brought freight to the department stores and picked up parcels for delivery to apartment houses along Lake Michigan. But speedier service in trucks put the railroad out of business, and the tunnel lay idle until the city found it could lay a new water main over the tracks. Now, other utilities are planning to use more sections of the tunnel. Space between city streets is almost more valuable than precious metals.

Chapter Three
Transportation Tunnels

Every day, millions of people travel to and from New York with hardly more than a glimpse of sunlight. They buy a railway ticket, put a token in a subway turnstile, or drive through one of the great tunnels that lie beneath one of the city's many rivers. Even people who walk to work can dart down a staircase and go sixteen blocks beneath Rockefeller Center without ever having to come up to the street. On a rainy day, New Yorkers, like human moles, will go through miles of tunnels around Grand Central Station in order to avoid getting wet.

77

Subways

Every weekday morning subway trains rumble along the tracks in New York City, picking up passengers on their way to work. By eight-thirty, trains are pulling into stations every ninety seconds, crammed with riders. Though there doesn't seem to be room for one more person, the subways will be still more crowded after five, when more than a million and a half people head for home. Visitors often stare unbelievingly as the station guards at Times Square or Grand Central stuff one more passenger into a jammed car and pull the sliding door shut. But New Yorkers are used to the crush. Many manage somehow to read their newspapers, even though they have to take a deep breath before turning its pages.

A ride on a modern, electrified subway is far different from a trip on the early steam-driven cars that chugged slowly through smoky tunnels. The first subway was built in London, England, over a hundred years ago, but many Americans were not convinced of the safety of underground trains. People argued that tunnels under the streets would weaken the foundations of their houses and any building over one story high would collapse. But in 1870, Alfred Beach got permission to build a pneumatic tunnel under two blocks in lower Manhattan. He was supposed to use the tube only for letters and parcels, but he made it large enough for an eight-foot passenger train. For a while people flocked to the one-car subway, which was blown back and forth by compressed air. But it was never more than an amusement ride, and Mr. Beach's dream of a network of pneumatic tubes hurrying people beneath our cities faded away.

LEFT: A subway train comes roaring down the tracks into a station.

NEXT PAGE: Passengers hurry on and off the train at an uncrowded time of day.

Thirty-five years later, when workmen were digging what they believed was Manhattan's first subway, they discovered Beach's brick tunnel. It was still in excellent condition, as if awaiting the passengers who never came.

If you stand in the front of a subway train, next to the motorman's cab, you can see the dark tunnels, and the steel tracks gleaming under the train's headlights. Signal lights flash by: green means the track is clear, orange is a warning to slow down, and red is the signal to stop. Should the train go past a red light, the brakes will lock automatically, bringing the subway to a halt.

The subways are like an overgrown set of toy trains, except that they get their power from a high-voltage third rail. Almost all the cars have motors in both the front and rear. The trains are put together in the yards by rolling the cars against each other so that the couplers join. Underneath the couplers are plates which pass current between the motors, so that when the motorman turns the engine on in the front car, all the other motors are started at the same time. At the end of the route, the motorman walks through the trains, opens up the cab in the rear of the last car, and starts the trip back. Most surface railroad trains which are driven by electric power could travel over newer subway tracks with only minor adjustments to the shoe which picks up the power from the third rail. In many places, though, the narrow tunnels would certainly not be wide enough to let a freight train through.

During a weekday in New York, there are almost nine thousand separate train trips along 720 miles of track. More passengers ride this transit system than climb aboard all the other subways and surface railroads in the country.

At night, most of the trains return to the yards where they are cleaned and made ready for the next day. As the cars are shifted around, any one may become the lead car on the early morning express. They are all equally able to do the job.

While it's the motorman who controls the speed of the train, the route is determined in signal towers which are spaced every few stations. Each tower has a huge switching board which shows every foot of track on its section of the line. The steady white lights indicate the open tracks, while the moving red lights mark each train as it travels over the rails. If there is a delay along his part of the line, a towerman can push in the buttons to cancel the old route and send the cars along a neighboring track.

One mistake with the routing buttons and a train may find itself heading in a strange direction. This happened in New York not too long ago, when a Brooklyn-bound train was sent by mistake under the East River and into Manhattan. The motorman of the wandering subway stopped long enough to call the dispatcher on an emergency call telephone. He was told that he couldn't turn around, for there were trains which belonged on the route behind him. So, on he went until the subway reached a larger station, where angry passengers got off to find a return train. Much later, the misguided subway was also returned to its home tracks and trainmen swear that its headlights seemed to be blushing.

Mistakes like this happen rarely, however, for subway employees are highly skilled at their jobs. The New York Transit Authority runs a school complete with switches, control boards, and a full-size section of track. Here, conductors get ready to answer hundreds of questions about how to get to different parts of the city. They also learn how to operate and, if necessary, repair the doors on the many different types of subway cars which have been bought over the years. In moments of emergency, when passengers must be led from a stalled train, it

83

is the conductor who makes sure that everyone gets to the surface safely.

Apprentice motormen also go to classes and become student drivers in mock subway cars. When they are good enough, the student motormen take out a special train which runs on an unused track in the Bronx. They practice with this train, until they can take the curves at the proper speed and know how to glide smoothly into a station. A sudden stop will not only jolt the passengers but also cause "flat tires." This happens when the metal wheel locks and goes skidding along the track, wearing the metal flat in one spot.

While the subway system has its own police force, including

The control board shows every train passing on this signal tower's section of track.

policewomen and plainclothes detectives, the most dangerous job is done by the men who repair the third rail. There can be no errors with this work, for the high-voltage current is on at all times. If trouble occurs during rush hours, the repairmen may have no more than a minute and a half to get their equipment ready and go to work on the live rail before another train comes along. Their only protection is a thin rubber mat which they must stand on every moment. All other workers keep their distance, for a careless touch of a hand by someone not on the rubber mat could be fatal. The part of the job which this

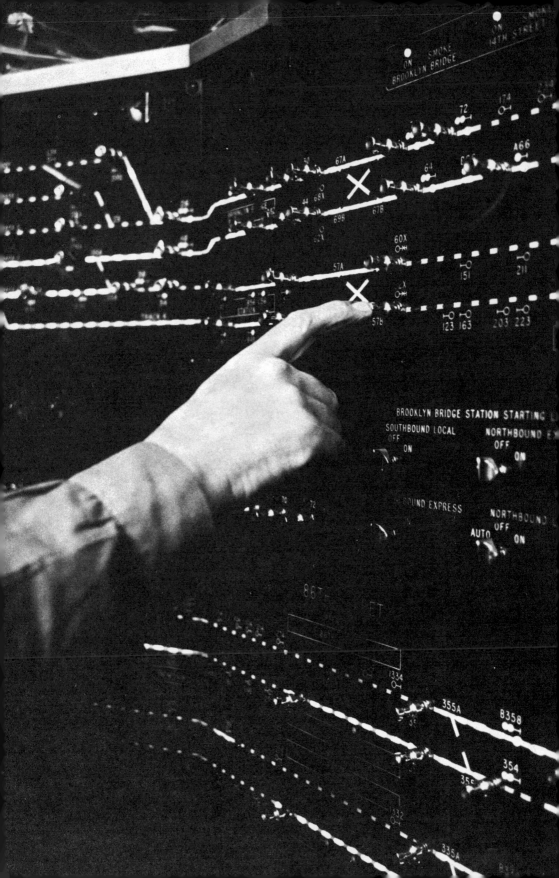

special crew dislikes is rescuing stray dogs and cats that wander into the tunnels and often crouch near the third rail. These animals must be pulled to safety with one quick motion without so much as a tail flicking the supercharged steel.

It takes a lot of sweeping, scrubbing, and painting to keep the stations clean, but what about the candy wrappers and old newspapers that blow onto the tracks? The Transit Authority has come up with an answer in the shape of the world's largest vacuum cleaner. It is a specifically built subway car with several long arms that reach into the dark corners of the tunnels as it goes slowly over the line. The vacuum cleaner car looks as if it came from some distant planet, but it is better than fifty strong cleaning men.

Late at night is the time to see other strange equipment. When snow falls through sidewalk gratings, a snow car blows it away and sprays alcohol on third rails to prevent icing. There are money trains with iron bars on the windows, and a car with ultrasonic devices for locating hidden cracks in the rails. Perhaps the slowest subway is the track-grinding train which creeps along at two miles an hour. Its ninety-six grinding wheels shoot sparks through the tunnel as they smooth the rough spots in the line.

One curious thing about subways is what the riders leave behind. Mink coats, bicycles, eyeglasses, false teeth, and musical instruments are only a few of the items which get sent to the Lost and Found. Several years back, a conductor discovered a tombstone in one of his cars. The Lost and Found thinks someone might have been trying to be funny, but they're not sure.

Five cities in the nation—Boston, New York, Philadelphia, Chicago, and Cleveland—have public subways. You can also

A closeup look at the board shows a switchman routing a train from one track to another.

Trainmen study switches on a track built in the subway school.

take a short ride in Washington, D.C., from both the Senate Office Building and the new House Office Building to the Capitol. When the bells ring for a vote, however, the subway becomes a private line so that congressmen will not be delayed on their way to the House or Senate floor.

San Francisco will soon be the next city to have underground travel. The trains will be automated, running without motormen or conductors. If the line works as expected, many other cities may install the same kind of automatic system. There is even some talk about building subway lines between cities, with trains that will rocket along at three hundred miles an hour . . . so hang on tight for a ride in the future.

Here, apprentice motormen learn how to operate the controls of a subway train.

NEXT PAGE: Sparks dance as the track-grinding train smooths the rail.

Railroads

At one time, all the railroads which entered New York traveled along above the avenues, trailing clouds of cinder and smoke. Not only were they unsightly, but they were also a hazard to horse-drawn vehicles, whose drivers didn't know enough to get out of the way of the iron monsters. Accidents along the West Branch of the New York Central on Twelfth Avenue happened so frequently that the street was called Death Avenue by the people who lived nearby. Finally, the City Fathers insisted that all railroad trains be put beneath the surface before they entered the downtown section of the city.

The most heavily traveled line goes down Park Avenue to Grand Central Terminal. When Cornelius Vanderbilt chose the

station site over one hundred years ago, Forty-second Street was uptown from the busy life of the city. His foresight was keen, however, because as New York grew to the north, the terminal found itself in the heart of Manhattan.

The railroad trains, now entirely driven by electric engines, dip into a tunnel at Ninety-sixth Street and travel the remaining two miles to the terminal underground. When they reach the main underground command post, Tower A, located in the heart of the station, the trains can be routed along one hundred and twenty-three separate tracks. Here, the suburban trains enter a downward grade which brings them to the station's lower level. Through traffic continues to the upper level platforms before heading off again to the Midwest or upstate New York.

The director of Tower A decides which of the forty-eight plat-

Here, trains plunge into the underground tunnel on the last leg of the journey to Grand Central Terminal.

NEXT PAGE: From Tower A, the main underground command post, the switchman routes trains over 123 separate tracks.

A steamliner swerves through the maze of track.

forms will be used by an incoming train. While it would seem that the daily schedule would make this job easy, unexpected delays and trains with added sections or extra cars cause endless changes.

Most of the station's platforms are stub ends, which means that a yard locomotive must pull the train away so that the engine can be uncoupled and shifted to the other end of the train. But eleven of the platform tracks connect to looprails, and the train can swing around in a wide circle and depart.

After an engine has made several long hauls, it must be inspected. It can be rolled over to a grease pit beneath the tracks where workmen, using bright lights, can carefully check the metal monsters above them.

Near the pit, on another spur track, is a giant electric crane. Should there be a derailment somewhere along the line, the crane is rushed from its underground home to where it is needed. Its twin booms, on each end, can lift a hundred-ton car and gently place it back on the tracks. When it is not busy in repair work, the crane is rented to construction companies which are building skyscrapers over the valuable property above the terminal. The steel foundations for the buildings that tower into the sky are actually planted next to the tracks. These girders are cased in blocks of lead before being placed in concrete blocks. The lead prevents the buildings from trembling as the trains roar by, by absorbing the vibrations.

On Track 28 you can see the massive roots of the Pan American Building as they bury themselves in the platform. Further up the track are the foundations of the famous Waldorf-Astoria Hotel. There is a private entrance to the hotel here, and trains have paused by its green door to let dukes and diplomats be whisked directly up to their suites. One railroad fan used to rent

These men work in a pit beneath the locomotives, making sure all engine parts are running properly.

Here, a huge crane lowers the foundation for skyscraper girders right beside the tracks in Grand Central.

NEXT PAGE: Sacks of mail drop from a conveyor belt, to be sorted and sent speeding throughout the United States.

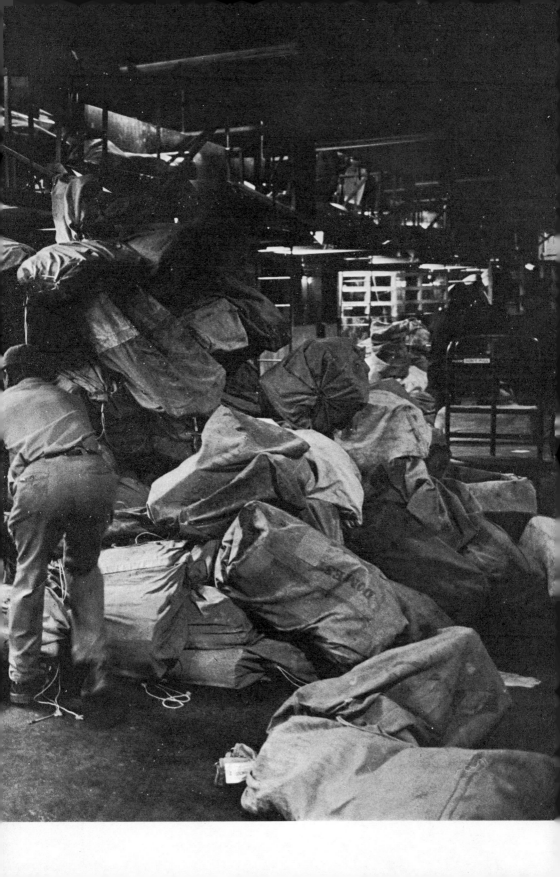

a New York Central car every Christmas and bring his friends to the hotel this way for a yearly party.

Besides taking freight and passengers, the railroads are the Number One carriers of the U. S. Mails. A Post Office next to Grand Central sends sacks of mail to the platforms on a moving belt. On some of the trains, letters going to a general area will be further sorted in a railroad mail car. When the weather is poor, bright orange bags are seen among the gray mail sacks. These hold airmail letters which have been grounded. Now they will go out by rail, for storm and fog will not stay the powerful locomotives. Newspapers are also great travelers, and on Saturday nights a blizzard of newsprint departs for far-off Sunday morning breakfast tables.

Once inside the terminal, a passenger can almost settle down permanently. Besides restaurants, clothing stores, and fancy groceries, there is an art gallery, a bookstore, and an underground movie house. Should you get tired, you can go directly through tunnels to any one of three large hotels. The terminal can also boast its own police force and a small hospital.

The terminal is so complete that there is a story some salesmen use it as an office. After buying the morning paper at one of the stands, and getting a quick cup of coffee, they take over a favorite telephone booth and go to work. Their sample cases and supplies can be easily stored in nearby lockers for twenty-five cents a day. They may also find it helpful to be close to forty-seven train platforms should they want to leave town in a hurry!

Underwater Tunnels

The other underground route of traveling into New York is through a tunnel. Deep under the water, there are a dozen

Grand Central Terminal, one of the world's largest underground railway stations.

subway tunnels, a railroad tunnel, and four tunnels for automobiles. Lincoln Tunnel, running under the Hudson River, is the largest of New York's underwater expressways.

Actually, it is two tunnels which were built at different times but placed beside each other. The older, larger tunnel has one double-lane roadway to New Jersey and another going to New York. As more cars jammed the highways, the second tunnel was dug, adding a tube which sends vehicles through in either direction, depending on the rush-hour traffic.

From this control center just outside the Manhattan entrance to the Lincoln Tunnel, all the signal lights can be instantly changed.

When motorists enter an underwater tunnel, they sometimes wonder how the white tiles can hold back the tremendous forces of the water. Actually, they are looking at the lining of the tunnel and not the concrete-and-steel outer shell which protects it. Between those two walls is the ventilation equipment. Huge exhaust fans clear out the deadly carbon monoxide fumes released by a car's exhaust pipe. Though this gas is odorless, drivers sometimes complain of smelling it, not knowing that a constant check keeps the air more free of monoxide than is a city street. What most people smell is the smoke from the diesel engines of heavy trucks. This nuisance is quickly

blown away by turning up the fans until the wind whistles through the tubes at thirty-five miles an hour.

The main task of men who work in tunnels is to keep traffic moving as fast as is safely possible. The signal lights in Lincoln Tunnel are electronically controlled and a TV camera scans the road for traffic troubles. A single car stalled during rush hour means that thousands of other automobiles will be delayed. Every few hundred feet, on a catwalk above the road, a policeman watches for just such a breakdown. As soon as there is trouble, he investigates. Is it a flat tire, a bad spark plug, or something more serious, like a broken axle? The patrol-

Any leaks? There is enough space between the tiles and the concrete-and-steel outer shell for this workman to make an inspection.

Cars speed through one of the tunnel's three tubes.

men are trained to make minor repairs and get the car moving again.

If they cannot handle the trouble, a call goes out to the emergency squad, which has men and equipment on both sides of the tunnel. This combat team enters the stalled lane from the opposite direction. A heavy-duty jeep with a hoist pulls out disabled automobiles, but for a trailer truck sprawled over the roadway or an accident involving several cars, the rescue crew uses a giant tractor on wheels. This tractor is so powerful that it can pull one huge truck and push another without straining.

On a hot summer day, when radiators begin to overheat, the emergency squad may haul out over a hundred cars. Besides this, they are ready to spread foam on a sudden fire, rescue pets who have jumped out of car windows, and, every once in a while, deliver a baby that wouldn't wait for the hospital. And all these services are free of charge.

With seven million pieces of white tile to keep clean, the maintenance men are also busy. Scrub-up time starts after midnight when one tube can be temporarily closed without inconveniencing motorists. A truck loaded with liquid soap rolls through the tunnel spraying the walls and roof. Then the tiles are rinsed with water until they sparkle.

Any of the tubes can be completely cleared of traffic in a matter of minutes. This is done if the President is making a trip through, or if emergency equipment like an ambulance or fire engine needs an open road. And what about pedestrians? The tunnel

LEFT: This tractor is powerful enough to move two stalled trucks from the tunnel at the same time.

NEXT PAGE: Tunnels must be kept clean, and this truck sprays the tiles with soap and water regularly.

111

police do not encourage people to walk the length of their tubes. They did make an exception, however, for the lady doctor from England who hiked across the United States a few years ago, and they let the Olympic runner carrying the symbolic torch past the toll booths. But everyone else needs fifty cents and an automobile.

Chapter Four
Bank Vaults

The most fascinating caverns in New York are also the most difficult to visit. These are the vast vaults below the banks in lower Manhattan, which hold riches that would make Ali Baba's treasure look puny. But no simple "Open, Sesame" will unlock these man-made vaults, for they are protected by thick steel and ever-watchful guards. As they are very deep below the level of the street, they can be easily protected against unwelcome intruders.

New York is the financial capital of the world, and beneath

the narrow streets where the early Dutch settlers first built their houses, lies the wealth of many nations. Wheat, oil, cotton, and machines shipped across oceans and deserts may be paid for with money that travels no further than a few yards.

The newest of these underground vaults is hidden ninety feet below the surface, in the Chase Manhattan Bank Building. To reach bedrock, hundreds of loads of dirt and debris were trucked away, leaving the largest hole ever dug in the city. When the foundations were solidly in place, a one-thousand-ton vault was bolted into the stone and concrete. Shortly after the Revolutionary War, a vast tidal wave swept away all the buildings in the same neighborhood. While the bank doesn't expect another wall of water, they are confident that their vault would remain immovable if one appears.

When the bank moved into this new building, convoys of armored cars brought securities and money from other branches. A ramp leads directly from the street into the top floor of the basement, so the steel-plated vehicles needn't stop on the streets to unload.

At the bottom of the bank's five basements is a giant safe surrounded by a room with bulletproof glass and an armed guard. The door of the safe weighs forty-five tons but it is so carefully balanced that when opened, you can move it back and forth with your little finger. However, you must wait for a time lock and know two combinations before the door opens at all.

Work in the basement of the bank goes on continuously. Computers hum, coins sift through automatic counters, and a printer as large as a newspaper press is typing out bank statements with hardly a pause. Not far off is a check-sorting machine that gobbles a million and a half checks each day and shoots them out into the right slot for each of the many branch banks. This machine, however, is fussy about working conditions, and if the air is too hot or too moist, its flashing blue and yellow lights go out.

Across the street from the Chase Manhattan Bank Building is one of the ten United States Federal Reserve Banks. They have the unusual task of being banker for the other banks. Just as you might open a savings account when you have a full jar of nickels and dimes, so regular banks take their extra money to the Federal Reserve Building for safekeeping.

Four basements below the street level of the New York Federal Reserve Bank is a room almost the size of a football field filled with gold bullion. There are so many bars of gold piled into separate cages that they do not look real. Only when you lift one of the small bricks that weighs twenty-seven pounds are you positive that you are in a treasure chamber.

More than thirteen billion dollars' worth of gold is kept in this vault. All the bullion belongs to foreign countries, and the United States stores and protects it free of charge. Should one nation that has a deposit want to pay another in gold, it instructs the Federal Reserve officials to make the transfer. Then the seals on their wire doors are opened and the right amount of gold moved from cage to cage. The workmen who actually lift the bullion wear steel-tipped shoes so that no toes will be broken if one of the heavy bars slips through their fingers.

In the vault above the gold room are stacks of neat rectangular packages wrapped in brown paper. It might be the inside of a supermarket warehouse, but the only thing here is money, which the Federal Reserve will issue to other banks. There is even a cageful of two-dollar bills which have never left the vault, because the public thinks they bring bad luck and prefers other denominations.

The strange thing about all these packages of money is that

117

Three feet of steel and a guard watch over this bank's vaults. (Photo by the
Chase Manhattan Bank)

they are worth no more than the cost of the paper and printing down in the sub-basement. This is because the Reserve Bank has not officially released these bills. If you had a brick of this unissued money, it would be like owning counterfeit currency.

Have you ever seen a million-dollar bill? Probably not, for they are used by banks when they transfer currency to each other. In the vault of the second sub-basement there are hundreds of these Federal Reserve Notes, packed tightly on revolving wheels, and the men who handle them work behind locked doors.

All three sub-basement vaults are carefully guarded and the doors to each underground safe need three men and two special keys before they can be opened. When the safe is closed, a hydraulic wheel lowers the door into a groove, turning it into a wall of steel, impossible to move without the keys.

A few feet down the corridor from the vault in the second sub-basement is a money-destroying room. Here, worn-out old bills of all denominations meet their end. They are counted, stacked, and then fed into a machine which punches holes in them and slices them in half lengthwise.

The men who do this job are able to tell when the money has been used mostly in the foreign countries near the equator. These bills stretch because of the high humidity and are a quarter of a size longer than similar notes. Unfortunately, they aren't any more valuable and are chopped in half just like their smaller brothers.

Those bills which have been issued by the New York Federal Reserve are taken to an incinerator next door and burned in a large furnace. Money burns slowly, and it is four or five hours before the bills are destroyed. To be extra sure, the bank sifts all the ashes through a fine screen to see that not even a scrap of paper remains.

A cageful of gold bars belonging to a foreign country.

121

The worn-out money issued by one of the other Federal Reserve Banks travels to Washington to be burned. The bank takes no chances that the old notes will fall into the wrong hands. The upper half of the bills are sent first, and not until a coded message tells of their safe arrival are the lower parts shipped out.

To watch over its vast sums of money, the bank has as many policemen as would be found in a medium-size city. These guards are experts with forty-fives and Thompson machine guns. There is a target range in one of the sub-basements, and the number of bull's-eyes in the targets shows clearly why no one has ever tried to rob this bank—not even Ali Baba's Forty Thieves.

LEFT: Stacked outside the cages, these gold bars are ready for shipment to another country, but their entire journey may be from one cage to another nearby.

NEXT PAGE: Here old bills are sliced in half. Both parts are headed for a fiery furnace.

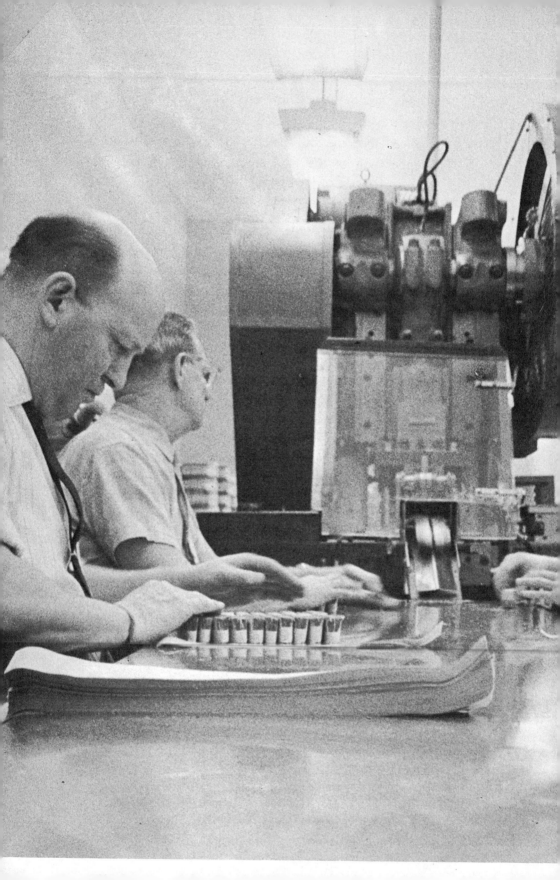

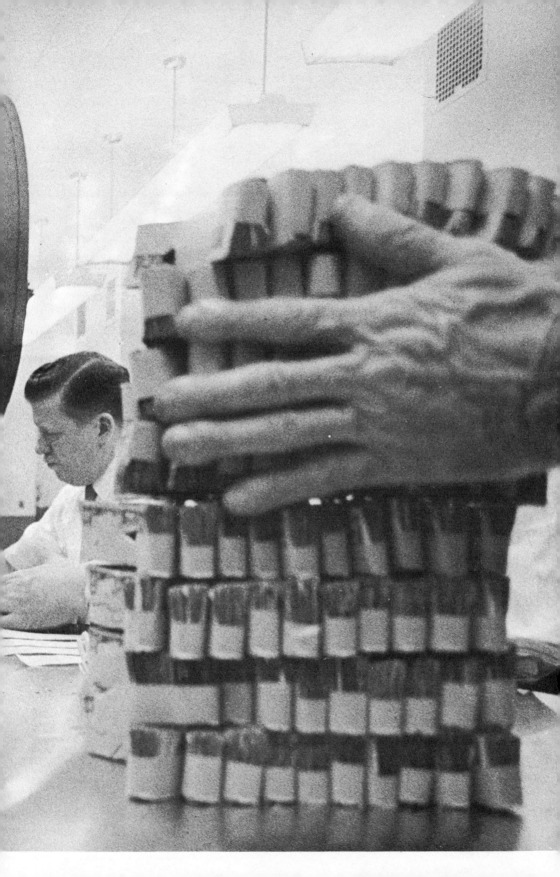

Chapter Five
The Future

The future belongs to the world of outer space and to the world of underground. People, houses, cars, and towns may all move below the surface. Already many major cities have underground garages, and New York is considering an expressway across lower Manhattan that may be entirely sub-surface. In Congress, there is some discussion about building a high-speed railroad line from Boston to Washington and putting it all underground.

Cities are making more use of the space under the streets.

Houston, Montreal, and Philadelphia have all recently built underground concourses. These air-conditioned corridors link private buildings, government centers, and stores.

And tomorrow's house may be below the lawn rather than on top of it. The recent World's Fair showed such a home, which had no problems with heat, snow, sticking windows, or leaky roofs. If you feel you must get outdoors, it is always up there somewhere.

Thousands of people today work in the brightly lit basements of skyscrapers without suffering any feeling of being closed in. And the men of our permanent base at Little America at the South Pole live under the ground for many months at a time.

There is also one more vast underground world which is now exciting man's imagination. This is the thousands of miles of uninhabited space underneath the surface of our oceans. Future cities may thrive under huge plastic bubbles which hold back tons of water. Travel would be by submarine express, and you could go from one city to another through special pressurized water locks. Children in tomorrow's schools who stare out windows may see a shark or a swordfish staring back.

But undersea or underground, bigger tunnels, faster communication routes, and new adventures await us in the future world below the surface.